Harry Potter

QUIZ BOOK

G2 Entertainment

G2 Entertainment, Unit 16, Beaufort Road, Reigate, Surrey, RH2 9DJ

Publishers Jules Gammond and Edward Adams

Design by Alex Young

Thanks goes to the following students at
Fittleworth Primary School
for all their hard work writing
the questions in this book even when
it seemed never ending:

Esme Sneller & Hattie McTeer

CONTENTS

QUESTIONS

ANSWERS

QUESTIONS

BOOK 1 -
The Philosopher's Stone

1. When was Harry Born?

2. What animal can professor McGonagall turn into?

3. Where does harry sleep when he's at the Dursley's?

4. How many presents does Dudley get for his birthday?

5. Who went with Dudley to the zoo?

6. What kind of snake does harry talk to at the zoo?

7. How old was Harry turning when Hagrid first arrived?

8. What colour was the icing on the cake Hagrid gave Harry?

9. What was the name of the teacher that Harry met at the Leaky Cauldron?

10. In Diagon Alley what was the first shop Harry visited?

11. In what shop did harry get his first wand?

12. What type of owl did harry get?

13. What number is the platform for Hogwarts express?

14. What food does Ron's mother pack him for the train journey to Hogwarts?

15. What spell does Ron use to try and turn his rat yellow?

16. Who escorted Harry from the train to Hogwarts?

17. Which house did the sorting hat consider putting harry in?

18. Who leads Ron and Harry to their dormitory?

19. What is Filch's cat called?

20. What was Harry's first class?

21. Who's class did Harry hate the most?

22. At flying lessons what made Harry fly when he wasn't supposed to?

23. Who was Gryffindors team captain for Quidditch?

24. Who first spotted the troll in the dungeon?

25. How did Hermione stop a teacher from Killing Harry at the quidditch match?

26. Which teacher did Hermione and Ron think was trying to kill Harry at the quidditch match?

27. Who is Hagrid referring to when he says he shouldn't have said that?

28. What did Hermione give Harry for Christmas?

29. Who almost catches Harry sneaking around in 'The Restricted Section' of the library?

30. What was the mirror that Harry found called?

31. Who was sat in the back of the room that contained the mirror?

32. When Nevelle's legs get locked by Malfoy what sweet did he give him?

33. On Nevelle's 'Chocolate Frog' there was Nicolas Flammel and who else?

34. What teachers did harry see talking in the Forbidden forest?

35. What kind of dragon did Hagrid 'win' from a stranger in the pub?

36. What pub was Hagrid visiting?

37. What musical instrument did Harry play to make fluffy go to sleep?

38. In the chamber below Fluffy what plant did Ron, Hermione and Harry get stuck in?

39. Once free of the plant what task was next?

40. When Ron, Harry and Hermione were playing chess what colour were they playing as?

41. What chess piece did Harry play as when playing wizards chess?

42. What beast was lying dead in the middle of the next chamber?

43. Who made the following task?

44. What colour was professor Quirrell's Turban?

45. Who saved Harry?

46. What flavour of 'Bertie Bot's Every Flavour Bean' did Dumbledore get?

47. Which one of Ron's brother's did they send Hagrid's dragon to?

48. What colour sweater did Mrs Weasley send Ron for Christmas?

49. Who sent Harry his invisibility cloak?

50. What is Ron's rat called?

51. When Ron Harry and Hermione found out about the three headed dog, who were they with?

52. What is the three headed dog called?

53. What did Hagrid name his Dragon?

54. What broom did Harry get given?

BOOK 2 -
The Chamber of Secrets

1. What colour was the car that Ron came in to save Harry?

2. What is the name of the Weasley's owl?

3. What department of 'The Ministry of Magic' does Mr Weasley work?

4. What was the name of the Weasley's House?

5. Who wrote the book 'Year with the Yeti?

6. What is the name of Ron's Little Sister?

7. What powder did they use to travel through the fireplace?

8. What shop did Harry initially land in?

9. Who came into the shop whilst Harry was hiding?

10. What was the name of the Alley in which Borgin and Burke's was situated?

11. Who found Harry in the Alley?

12. What was the name of Gilderoy Lockharts Auto Biography?

13. Why did Harry and Ron miss the Hogwarts Express?

14. What did Snape want to happen to Ron and Harry for driving the flying car to school?

15. What did Ron receive in the post from his mum?

16. What type of plants did they have to re-pot?

17. What came out of Ron's mouth when a spell meant for Draco backfired?

18. What is a mudblood?

19. What did Harry have to do for his detention?

20. What's the name of the ghost who lives in the girl's bathroom?

21. Who was the first to be 'petrified'?

22. What's a squib?

23. What phobia does Ron have?

24. Who did Harry, Ron and Hermione first suspect to be the heir?

25. What hit Harry off his broom during the quidditch match?

26. What did Madam Pomfrey use to help Harry's bones grow back?

27. What does Dobby wear to mark the 'house-elf's enslavement?

28. What club did Dumbledore as Lockhart to start?

29. What type of charm is 'Epelliarmus'?

30. What special language does Harry know?

31. Which ghost got petrified?

32. What is the name of Dumbledore's Phoenix?

33. What do Phoenix's do when it's time for them to die?

34. What is special about aa Phoenix's tears?

35. Where did Mr and Mrs Weasley go at Christmas time?

36. What did they use to knock Crabbe and Goyle out?

37. Who was Hermione trying to turn into when she took the polyjuice potion?

38. How long had it been since the Chamber of Secrets had been opened?

39. What 'hit' Myrtle on the head?

40. What is Tom Riddle's Middle Name?

41. What saved Harry and Ron from Aragog?

42. What does a Basalisk Flee from?

43. Who was taken down into the chamber?

44. What spell did Lockhart use to remove Ron and Harry's Memories?

45. Why did Harry have to go into the chamber alone?

46. What did Fawkes bring with him to the chamber?

47. What did Harry use to destroy the diary?

48. Who's sword did Harry Pull out of the sorting hat?

49. Who had given Ginny the diary?

50. How many house points did Harry and Ron get each?

BOOK 3 -

The Prisoner of Azkaban

1. What did Hagrid give Harry for his birthday?

2. Where the 'Third-years' allowed to visit at certain weekends?

3. Which Aunt came to visit the Dursley's?

4. What was the name of the driver on the Knight Bus?

5. Who had escaped Azkaban?

6. Who met Harry at the Leaky Cauldron?

7. What did Hermione buy from the Magical Menagerie Shop?

8. What did Lupin give Harry after Harry experienced the dementor on the train?

9. What lesson did Hagrid teach?

10. What was the password for the Gryffindor Common room?

11. What was their first lesson?

12. What did professor Trelawny see in Harry's 'cup'?

13. What type of creature is Buckbeak?

14. Where do boggarts like to be?

15. What did Ron add roller skates to when faced with a Boggart?

16. What colour is Neville's grandma's handbag?

17. What day was the first trip to Hogsmeade?

18. Who scared the fat lady out of her painting?

19. What creature did Professor Snape teach about when he stood in for Lupin?

20. What did Fred and George give Harry as an early Christmas Present?

21. What did Ron Hermione and Harry buy at 'The Three Broomsticks'?

22. What broomstick did Harry get for Christmas?

23. What did Harry think of to get his 'Expecto Patronum' spell to work against the boggart dementor?

24. Who won the quidditch match of Ravenclaw vs Gryffindor?

25. Who dressed up as dementors to distract Harry at the quidditch match?

26. Who accidentally helped Sirius Black get into the Gryffindor Dormitories?

27. Which house won the quidditch cup?

28. During Harry's exam with professor Trelawney what did he say he could see in the crystal ball?

29. At what time do they plan to execute Buckbeak?

30. Where abouts did Hagrid tether Buckbeak?

31. Who did the black dog drag into the gap of the Whomping Willow?

32. Where does the tunnel under the Whomping Willow lead to?

33. Who was Scabbers the rat?

34. What was James Potter's nickname?

35. Which two teachers arrived at the Shrieking Shack?

36. What kind of creature is Lupin?

37. What did Sirius offer Harry?

38. What 'animal' did Harry see after being attacked by the dementors?

39. Who's room was Sirius Black locked in?

40. How many turns does Dumbledore suggest to Hermione?

41. What is the hour glass 'thing' called?

42. Who gave the time-turner to Hermione?

43. Who did Harry think he saw conjuring the patronus?

44. Who actually conjured the patronus that saved Harry, Hermione and Sirius?

45. What does Ron call a telephone?

46. What does Sirius give Ron?

47. Which subject does Hermione dislike?

BOOK 4 -

The Goblet of Fire

1. What is the village called where Riddle House is located?

2. What was the name of the Riddle's gardener?

3. Who did Harry write to about his scar burning?

4. What food did MRs Weasley send to Harry while he was at the Dursley's?

5. What job do Hermione's parents have?

6. What two countries were in the world cup Quidditch match that Harry, Ron and Hermione went to watch?

7. How did the Weasley's arrive at the Dursley's?

8. What happened to Dudley's tongue after eating one of Fred's 'toffees'?

9. What is Ron's owl called?

10. What was the portkey that took them to the world cup?

11. What position does Viktor Krum play?

12. The Bluebottle was advertised at the Quidditch World Cup but what is 'The Bluebottle?

13. How many Quidditch World Cups had there been before?

14. What were the Bulgarian Mascots?

15. What shape is the dark mark?

16. Who's wand was used to conjure the dark mark in the sky?

17. What are Voldermort's supporters called?

18. How many Golden hands did the Weasley's grandfather clock have?

19. What school did Draco's dad want to send him to?

20. Who was throwing water bombs when they arrived at Hogwarts?

21. What is the name of Colin Creevy's brother?

22. What was the minimum age for entering the Triwizard Tournament?

23. Gryffindor had their first lesson with which other house?

24. What did Moody turn Draco into?

25. How many Unforgivable curses are there?

26. What colour is the Beauxbatons uniform?

27. What does Dumbledore draw around the Goblet of Fire?

28. What is the name of the news reporter that interviewed Harry?

29. What kind of quill did the reporter use?

30. What are the four types of Dragons used in the first task?

31. Which Dragon did Fleur have to face?

32. What type of dog did Cedric transfigure a rock into?

33. What spell did Harry use in the first task?

34. What word did Harry give Rita Skeeter after the scoring of the first task?

35. What three ways can Blast-Ended Skrewts harm you?

36. What did the champions have to do with the egg to open it?

37. Who did Ron go with to the Yule Ball?

38. Who does Viktor have to save in the second task?

39. What was the plant Harry ate to help him with the second task?

40. What day and time did Sirius ask Harry to meet him in Hogsmeade?

41. What food did Ron ask the house elf to bring him just after breakfast?

42. Who does Nagini bite in Harry's 'dream'?

43. Where did Harry find himself when he looked inside Dumbledore's pensieve?

44. What is the answer to the riddle that the sphinx gave to Harry?

45. Where did the cup take Harry and Cedirc?

46. What happened to Voldermort's mum?

47. What was the colour of the jet of light that left Harry's wand when he duelled with Voldermort?

48. How many locks did the trunk have in Moody's office?

49. Who was pretending to be Mad eye Moody?

50. Who's animagus was a beetle?

51. Who is Snuffles?

BOOK 5 -
The Order of the Phoenix

1. Who can see thestrals?

2. What are thestrals?

3. What attacks Harry in the alleyway in little whinging?

4. what did harry find out about Mrs fig?

5. Who received a Howler at the Dursley's?

6. What can be found at number twelve, Grimmauld Place, London?

7. What had Fred and George invented as a useful tool to listen in on the meetings?

8. Who does 12 Grimmauld Place belong to?

9. Who is Voldermort scared of?

10. Where does Sirius keep Buckbeak?

11. What was Sirius' brother called?

12. What was the red telephone box used for?

13. What is the number that Mr Weasley dials to gain entry?

14. Which courtroom did Harry's hearing happen in?

15. What was waiting for Mr Weasley in Bethnal Green?

16. Which two out of the main three became Gryffindor Prefects?

17. Which broom did Ron ask his mum to buy?

18. What colour is associated with Professor Umbridge?

19. What was unusual about Professor Umbridge's lessons?

20. What did Professor Umbridge give Harry a detention for?

21. What did Hermione threaten Fred and George with when giving 'Fainting Fancies' to first years?

22. What did Harry have to write in his detentions with Professor Umbridge?

23. Who told Ron to stay away from Harry?

24. What happened to girls' dormitory stairs when Ron stepped on the 6th step?

25. What part of Hedwig became injured?

26. Who suggested 'The Room of Requirement' to Harry?

27. What does DA stand for?

28. What was the first spell Harry got the DA to practise?

29. Which Hogwarts house did Hermione almost end up in?

30. What position does Ron play in Quidditch?

31. Where do giants live?

32. What's a Gurg?

33. Who replaced Harry as seeker?

34. Who kissed Harry under the Mistletoe?

35. What is the name of the hospital that Arthur Weasley went to?

36. What type of 'muggle treatment did Arthur Weasley have done to his wound?

37. Who was Neville visiting at the hospital?

38. Who tortured Neville's parents?

39. What did Snape give private lessons to Harry in?

40. What are the workers at the Department of Mysteries also known as?

41. How many Death Eaters escaped Azkaban?

42. What was the name of the café Harry and Cho went to on Valentine's day?

43. Who replaces Dumbledore as Head Teacher at Hogwarts?

44. What was the nickname James Potter had for Professor Snape?

45. Who's Grawp?

46. Who sent the dementor's after Harry ?

47. What was contained in the large glass tank full of green liquid?

48. Who did they go to the Ministry of Magic to save?

49. What shape was the 'prophecy'?

50. Who killed Sirius?

51. How was Sirius related to Bellatrix Lestrange?

BOOK 6 -

The Half Blood Prince

1. Which compartment did Harry share lunch with Slughorn?

2. Who did Snape form The Unbreakable Vow with?

3. What did Harry notice about Dumbledore's hand when he was at 4 Privet Drive?

4. What is Dumbledore's favourite flavour jam?

5. What was Horace Slughorn pretending to be when Harry and Dumbledore entered his house?

6. What does Dumbledore tell Harry to keep with him at all times?

7. What is Arthur Weasley's dearest ambition?

8. What does Molly Weasley liked to be called by Arthur?

9. What was the new name given to Buckbeak?

10. What is the name of Fred & George's shop?

11. Who saved Harry from being stuck on Hogwart's Express?

12. Who is Gryffindor's Quidditch Captain?

13. What type of potion is Armotentia?

14. What was Katie Bell carrying that caused her to be cursed?

15. What did Harry supposedly spike Ron's juice with before the quidditch match?

16. What was the Gryffindor 'festive' password for the common room?

17. Who did Harry invite to Slughorn's Christmas party?

18. What is the name of the werewolf that bit Lupin?

19. What was written on the necklace Ron was given by Lavendar for Christmas?

20. What did Dumbledore ask Harry to get from Horace Slughorn?

21. What are the three Ds Twycross teaches in Apparation classes?

22. What did Harry give Ron for his birthday?

23. What was the name of the orphanage that Tom Riddle grew up in?

24. What was Voldemort's mum called?

25. What did Harry use to save Ron when he was poisoned?

26. Who replaced Ron as keeper in Quidditch?

27. Which two house elves were fighting in the hospital wing?

28. Where did Tom Riddle work when he first left Hogwarts?

29. What was the job Tom Riddle wanted after finishing at Hogwarts?

30. What was the name of Hepzibah Smith's house elf?

31. What did Ron mean to write when he wrote 'Dugbogs'?

32. What room doesn't appear on the Marauders map?

33. What did Ron leave behind to cause him to fail his apparition test?

34. Where abouts did Hagrid choose to bury Aragog?

35. Who was present at the burial of Aragog?

36. What does a person conceal inside a Horcrux?

37. Which Horcrux had Dumbledore destroyed?

38. What liquid did they have to try and turn into wine during a Charms lesson?

39. Where did Harry hide his copy of Advanced Potion-Making?

40. What did Ginny tell people Harry had tattooed across his chest?

41. Who overheard Professor Trelawny's prophecy in the Hog's head?

42. What kind of payment did the 'cave' door require?

43. What did Dumbledore discover that helped him and Harry over the Lake?

44. What colour was the potion in the basin?

45. What did Dumbledore summon to repel the inferi?

46. What 'Horcrux' did they find in the cave?

47. Who killed Dumbledore?

48. Who was supposed to kill Dumbledore?

49. Who was the 'Half Blood Prince'?

50. What creatures sang at Dumbledore's funeral?

BOOK 7 -

The Deathly Hallows

1. Who did Snape arrive with to the Malfoy's?

2. What is the core of Malfoy's wand?

3. Who was held captive above the table at the Malfoy's Mansion?

4. How many 'Harry Potters' were there when they moved Harry to the safe house?

5. What colour was Harry's polyjuice potion once he added his hairs?

6. What names did Hermione give her parents when she modified their memories?

7. What was a traditional gift to receive when 'you come of age'?

8. What was Harry's birthday cake?

9. What did Dumbledore leave Ron in his will?

10. What job did Gregorovitch have?

11. Who was R.A.B?

12. What did Harry's 'Wanted' poster say they wanted Harry for?

13. Who became Headmaster at Hogwarts?

14. Who has the real Locket?

15. Who is 'Undesirable No. 1'?

16. What happened to Ron when they escaped the 'Ministry of Magic'?

17. Essence of what healed Ron's wound?

18. What did Ginny, Luna & Neville try to steal from Snape's office?

19. Where was Godric Gryffindor's birth place?

20. What did Bathilda Bagshot turn into?

21. What lead Harry to the pool that had the sword of Gryffindor?

22. What shape was the door knocker on the Lovegood's door?

23. What did Xenophilius (Luna's dad) say she was catching down at the river?

24. What did 'Death' make the eldest brother's wand out of?

25. What did the third brother ask for?

26. How you become the 'Master of Death?

27. Which five people had Luna painted on her bedroom ceiling?

28. What was the name of the radio channel that was against the 'Dark Lord'?

29. Which word was a 'Taboo'?

30. Who did Harry say his name was when they were caught by snatchers?

31. Where was Voldemort's base?

32. Who was locked in the cellar with Luna?

33. Who came to save them from Malfoy's Manor?

34. Who lives at Shell Cottage?

35. What did Bellatrix use to kill Dobby?

36. What were the last two words Dobby said?

37. What did Tonks and Lupin name their baby?

38. Who did Hermione transform into to break into Gringotts?

39. What Horcrux did they find in Bellatrix's vault?

40. What creature did they use to escape Gringotts?

41. Where did they meet Dumbledore's brother?

42. Who killed 'The Grey Lady'?

43. Where had Tom Riddle hidden the Diadem?

44. Who was already inside the room of requirement?

45. Where was Voldemort hiding with Nagini?

46. What did Snape give Harry before he died?

47. Who did Harry ask to kill Nagini?

48. Who checked whether Harry was really dead?

49. Who was the true master of the Elder Wand after Dumbledore?

50. What did Harry use to repair his wand?

51. How many years later is the final chapter set?

52. How many children did Harry and Ginny have?

Magical World General Knowledge

1. What is Filch's first name?

2. What are the four founding professors of Hogwarts?

3. What does the Hogwarts Motto mean in English?

4. What is Hagrid's original job at Hogwarts?

5. What does OWLs stand for?

6. What is Hufflepuffs house animal?

7. What are the colours for Ravenclaw?

8. How many different 'Defence Against the Dark Arts' teachers were there during the series?

9. Who was the headmaster before Dumbledore?

10. What is the house ghost for Slytherin called?

11. Other than Dumbledore who else was a headteacher at Hogwarts during the series?

12. What is the typical age of a seventh year student at Hogwarts?

13. What does the name 'Dumbledore' mean?

14. What is the name of the joke shop in Hogsmeade?

15. What does the shop 'Honeydukes' sell?

16. Where can you find Florean Fortescue's Ice Cream Parlour?

17. What is the pub called that acts as an entrance to Diagon Alley?

18. What's the name of the main newspaper?

19. What can you buy at Flourish and Blotts?

20. The Hogwarts Express starts at Platform 9 & 3/4, but where does it end?

21. What are the front doors of Hogwarts made of?

22. What is unique about Hogsmeade?

23. What is the dangerous alley near to Diagon Alley?

24. What hazard can be found on the hidden staircase at Hogwarts?

25. Which room in Hogwarts are you trying to enter when you tickle the pear in the fruit bowl?

26. There are 142 what in Hogwarts?

27. How many floors does Hogwarts have?

28. What time does the Hogwarts express leave Kings Cross?

29. What would muggle see if they came across Hogwarts?

30. What kind of creatures own and operate Gringotts?

31. Which Hogwarts professor has the first name of Wilhelmina?

32. How many different types of ball are used in Quidditch?

33. How many players are there in a quidditch team?

34. What breed of owl was Hedwig?

35. What type of car was the Weasley's 'Enchanted car?

36. What type of vegetable earring does Luna Lovegood wear?

37. What does Dumbledore believe is more powerful than magic?

38. What was Dumbledore's brother called?

39. Who is the author of 'Fantastic Beasts and Where to Find Them'?

40. Which Quidditch team did Ron Support?

41. How is the Grey Lady related to Rowena Ravenclaw?

42. What is the killing curse?

43. Who gave Professor Slughorn a pet fish?

44. What colour is a Howler?

45. What is an Aurora?

46. What kind of memory does a snitch have?

47. What does the gemino curse do?

48. What do Death Eaters have on their forearm?

49. What does a Pensieve do?

50. Where was the Pensieve located at Hogwarts?

51. What kind of charm requires a powerful happy memory?

52. How should you greet a Hippogrith?

53. Who is the author of A History of Magic?

54. In what year did the battle of Hogwarts occur?

55. How many ghosts live at Hogwarts?

56. How do you open the Marauders map ?

57. Who is the matron at Hogwarts?

58. How many values does each Hogwarts house have?

59. Who is responsible for cooking and cleaning at Hogwarts?

60. In what year do students travel form Hogsmeade station to Hogwarts by boat?

61.   What shapes make up the Deathly Hallows symbol?

62.   Who makes every flavour beans?

63.   What does the 'Lumos' spell do?

64.   Who calls Dumbledore 'Dumblydore?

65.   What does the potion Veritaserum do?

66.   How many children do the Weasley's have?

67.   What is the first spell they learn at Hogwarts?

68.   How many Ministers for magic were there throughout the series?

69.   Pictures of 'who' are hung in the headmasters office?

70.   What does Hagrid keep inside a pink umbrella?

71.   What is Lily Potter's Maiden name?

The Author
J K Rowling

1. What year was J K Rowling born?

2. What does the 'K' stand for in her name?

3. What did J K Rowling use to type up the manuscript for the first book?

4. How many publishers rejected the original Harry Potter book?

5. What book did J K Rowling write for adults?

6. What is J K Rowling's male author name?

7. What is the Name of the two-part play she co-authored about Harry Potter?

8. What is the name of the website J K Rowling set up to release further Harry Potter material?

9. Where was J K Rowling when she came up with the names for the Hogwarts Houses?

10. What was J K Rowling's main request when approached by the film directors?

11. Who did J K Rowling base the character of Severus Snape on?

12. What year was the first Harry Potter book released?

13. Which Hogwarts house is J K Rowling's favourite?

14. Which character has J K Rowling said is most like herself?

On The Film Set

1. How Many Harry Potter films have been made?

2. Who did Tom Felton (The actor who played Draco) audition for originally?

3. How many Owls played Hedwig?

4. How many buses were used to build the 'Knight Bus'?

5. What was unique about the actress that played 'Moaning Myrtle'?

6. During the filming of the Chamber of Secrets a nurse had to be called on set because of an outbreak of what?

7. Which production company own the rights to Harry Potter?

8. How many pairs of glasses did Daniel Radcliffe go through in the making of the films?

9. What phobia does Rupert Grint have?

10. What did Daniel Radcliffe discover he was allergic to when filming The Philosophers Stone?

11. Which film is the longest in the series?

12. How were the candles made to appear as though they were floating?

13. What ball was used to portray Dobby whilst filming?

14. What inspired the design for Dobby's ears in the movies?

15. Where is the Harry Potter studio in London?

16. What year was the first film released?

17. Which actor played multiple roles including the voice of another?

18. In the films what happens to Voldemort's robe each time a horcrux is destroyed?

19. In the films how tall was Hagrid portrayed?

True or False

1. Aberforth Dumbledore's patronus was a goat?

2. James Potter was Head Boy whilst at Hogwarts?

3. Photographs in the magical world are static like those in the muggle world?

4. Severus Snape met Lily Potter before they went to Hogwarts?

5. Petunia Evan's (lily's sister) wrote a letter to Hogwarts asking if she could attend?

6. Mandrakes were fatal because of their poisonous sap?

7. Werewolves transform on the nights of a full moon?

8. The Tales of Beedle the Bard contains 10 different stories?

9. Bellatrix Lestrange was related to Tonks?

10. Voldemort was a mud-blood?

11. The whomping willow was over 500 years old?

12. The fat Lady never moved from her painting?

13. Ron sat on the Knight during their game of Wizards chess in their first year?

14. Catching the snitch means you automatically win the game?

15. In Dumbledore's youth he came across a vomit flavoured every flavour bean?

16. Harry freed Dobby by giving him a t-shirt?

17. Hermione was born in Godric's Hollow?

18. Luna Lovegood wears a Lion Headress to a quidditch match?

19. Neville had a pet cat?

20. Percy lived in Egypt?

21. The Three Broomsticks Pub was in Diagon Alley?

22. The wizard on Harry's first Chocolate Frog card was Dumbledore?

23. The Slytherin colours are green and black?

24. Voldemort killed Harry in the Forbidden Forest?

25. Sirius was sent to Azkaban because he supposedly murdered 50 people?

26. The Basilisk had red eyes?

27. Peter Pettigrew cut off his right hand for Voldemort?

28. Harry's second son was called Albus Sirius Potter

29. Luna Lovegood was 9 years old when her mother died?

30. When transporting Harry to a safe house Ron pairs up with Madeye Moody?

31. Dumbledore was offered the job of Minster for Magic several times?

32. Helga Hufflepuffs cup is destroyed by the sword of Gryffindor?

33. Professor Flitwick taught Charms?

34. Unicorn blood is silver?

35. Ron's first girlfriend was Cho Chang?

36. Neville became a teacher at Hogwarts?

37. Hermione's parents moved to Austria?

38. Arthur Weasley collected batteries?

39. Professor McGonogall never gave Harry a detention?

40. The Weasley's kept chickens?

41. Neville's toad is called Trevor?

ANSWERS

BOOK 1 – THE PHILOSOPHER'S STONE

1. 31st July 1980
2. Cat
3. Cupboard under the stairs
4. 36
5. Piers Polkiss
6. Boa constrictor
7. Eleven
8. Green
9. Quirrell
10. Gringgotts
11. Ollivanders
12. Snowy owl
13. 9 and 3/4
14. Corned beef
15. Sunshine Daisies, butter mellow. Turn this stupid fat rat yellow.
16. Hagrid
17. Slytherin
18. Percy Weasley
19. Mrs Norris
20. Potions Class
21. Professor Snape's
22. Trying to retrieve Neville's remembrall from Draco Malfoy
23. Oliver Wood
24. Professor Quirrel
25. Set alight Snape's Cloak
26. Professor Snape
27. Fluffy
28. A large box of chocolate frogs
29. Filch
30. The Mirror of erised
31. Dumbledore
32. Chocolate Frog
33. Dumbledore

34. Professor Snape & Professor Quirrel
35. Norwegian Ridgeback
36. Leaky Cauldron
37. A Flute
38. Devil's Snare
39. The Flying Keys
40. Black
41. Bishop
42. Troll
43. Professor Snape
44. Purple
45. Dumbledore
46. Earwax
47. Charlie
48. Maroon
49. Dumbledore
50. Scabbers
51. Hagrid
52. Fluffy
53. Norbert
54. Nimbus 2000

BOOK 2 – THE CHAMBER OF SECRETS

1. Turquoise (blue)
2. Errol
3. The Misuse of Muggle Artefacts
4. The Burrow
5. Gilderoy Lockhart
6. Ginny
7. Floo Powder
8. Borgin and Burkes
9. Lucious and Draco Malfoy
10. Knockturn Alley
11. Hagrid
12. Magical Me
13. They couldn't get through the wall
14. To be Expelled
15. A Howler

16. Mandrakes
17. Slugs
18. Someone who is muggle born with non-magical parents
19. Answer Lockhart's fan mail
20. Moaning Myrtle
21. Mrs Norris
22. Someone born into a magical family with no powers of their own
23. Spiders
24. Draco Malfoy
25. Bludger
26. Skele-Gro
27. A Pillowcase
28. Duelling Club
29. Disarming Charm
30. Parseltongue
31. Nearly Headless Nick
32. Fawkes
33. Burst into flame
34. They have healing power
35. Egypt to visit their son Bill
36. Cakes filled with a sleeping draught
37. Millicent Bulstrode
38. 50 years
39. Tom Riddle's Diary
40. Marvolo
41. The Weasley's Car
42. The Crowing of a Rooster
43. Ginny Weasley
44. Obliviate

45. Lockhart's blast caused a cave in that separated Harry from Ron and Lockhart
46. The Sorting Hat
47. Basilisk Fang
48. Godric Gryffindor
49. Lucious Malfoy
50. 200

BOOK 3 – THE PRISONER OF AZKABAN

1. Monster Book of Monsters
2. Hogsmede
3. Aunt Marge
4. Ernie
5. Sirius Black
6. Cornelius Fudge
7. A cat (Crookshanks)
8. Large piece of chocolate
9. Care of Magical Creatures
10. Fortuna Major
11. Divination
12. The Grim
13. Hippogriff
14. In dark, enclosed spaces
15. A spider
16. Red
17. 31st October - Halloween
18. Sirius Black
19. Werewolves
20. The Marauders Map
21. Butterbeer
22. The Firebolt

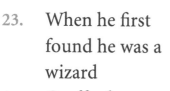

23. When he first found he was a wizard
24. Gryffindor
25. Draco Malfoy, Crabbe & Goyle
26. Neville Longbottom
27. Gryffindor
28. A Hippogriff
29. At Sunset
30. In a pumpkin patch
31. Ron
32. The Shrieking Shack
33. Peter Pettigrew
34. Prongs
35. Professor Lupin & Professor Snape
36. Werewolf
37. To have Harry live with him

38. A Stag
39. Professor Flitwick
40. Three
41. A time turner
42. Professor McGonagall
43. His dad
44. Harry
45. Fellytone
46. An Owl
47. Divination

BOOK 4 – THE GOBLET OF FIRE

1. Little Hangleton
2. Frank
3. Sirius
4. A fruitcake and pasties
5. Dentists
6. Ireland vs Bulgaria

7. Through the fireplace
8. It went purple and grew very large
9. Pigwidgeon
10. A Boot
11. Seeker
12. A broom
13. 421
14. Veela
15. A skull
16. Harry's
17. Death Eaters
18. Nine
19. Durmstrang
20. Peeves
21. Dennis
22. 17
23. Hufflepuff
24. A Ferret
25. Three
26. Pale Blue
27. An age line
28. Rita Skeeter
29. Quick Quotes Quill
30. Welsh Green, Chinese Fireball, Swedish Shortsnout & Hungarian Horntail
31. Welsh Green
32. A Labrador
33. Accio
34. Goodbye
35. Sting, Suckers and fire blasting ends
36. Go underwater with it
37. Padma Patil
38. Hermione
39. Gillyweed
40. Saturday at 2pm
41. An Éclair
42. Mr Weasley

43. Sitting on a Bench at the end of a room
44. A Spider
45. A graveyard
46. She died while giving birth
47. Red
48. Seven
49. Barty Crouch
50. Rita Skeeter
51. Sirius Black

BOOK 5 – THE ORDER OF THE PHOENIX

1. People who have witnessed death.
2. They are horse-like creatures that pull the carriages to Hogwarts

3. Dementors
4. She is a squib
5. Petunia
6. The Headquarters of the Order of the Phoenix
7. Extendable ears
8. Sirius Black
9. Dumbledore
10. In his mother's bedroom
11. Regulus
12. As a visitors entrance to the Ministry of Magic
13. 62442
14. 10
15. A vomiting toilet
16. Hermione and Ron
17. A Cleansweep
18. Pink
19. They didn't involve any magic

20. For saying that Lord Voldemort had returned
21. A letter to their mum
22. I must not tell lies'
23. Percy
24. A Klaxon sounded and the stairs became a slide
25. Wing
26. Dobby
27. Dumbledore's Army
28. Expelliarmus
29. Ravenclaw
30. Keeper
31. Mountains
32. A Chief Giant
33. Ginny Weasley
34. Cho Chang
35. St Mungo's
36. Stitches
37. His parents
38. Bellatrix Lestrange
39. Occlumency
40. Unspeakables
41. 10
42. Madam Puddifoot's
43. Professor Umbridge
44. Snivellus
45. Hagrid's half brother
46. Professor Umbridge
47. Brains
48. Sirius Black
49. Sphere
50. Bellatrix Lestrange
51. They were cousins

BOOK 6 – THE HALF BLOOD PRINCE

1. C
2. Narcissa Malfoy
3. That it was blackened & shrivelled
4. Raspberry
5. An armchair
6. The invisibility cloak
7. To find out how aeroplanes stay up
8. Mollywobbles
9. Witherwings
10. Weasleys' Wizard Wheezes
11. Tonks
12. Harry
13. A love potion
14. An Opal necklace
15. Lucky Potion
16. Baubles
17. Luna Lovegood
18. Fenrir Greyback
19. My Sweetheart
20. A memory
21. Destination, Determination & Deliberation
22. Quidditch keeper Gloves
23. Wool Orphanage
24. Merope Gaunt
25. A Bezoar
26. McLaggen
27. Kreacher and Dobby
28. At Borgin & Burkes
29. Teacher at Hogwarts for defence against the dark arts
30. Hokey
31. Dementors

BOOK 7 – THE DEATHLY HALLOWS

12. Questioning about the death of Albus Dumbledore
13. Snape
14. Dolores Umbridge
15. Harry Potter
16. He was Splinched
17. Dittany
18. The Sword of Gryffindor
19. Godric's Hollow
20. A Snake
21. A silver Doe
22. An Eagle
23. Plimpies
24. Elder
25. Death's cloak of invisibility
26. Have all 3 of the deathly Hallows
27. Harry, Ron, Hermione, Ginny & Neville
28. Potterwatch
29. Voldemort
30. Vernon Dudley
31. At the Malfoy Mansion
32. Ollivander
33. Dobby
34. Bill & Fleur
35. A knife
36. Harry Potter
37. Ted Remus Lupin
38. Bellatrix
39. Helga Hufflepuff's Cup
40. A dragon
41. Hog's Head
42. The Bloody Baron

43. In the room of requirement
44. Draco, Crabbe & Goyle
45. The Shrieking Shack
46. A collection of his memories
47. Neville
48. Narcissa Malfoy
49. Draco Malfoy
50. The Elder Wand
51. 19
52. Three

THE MAGICAL WORLD GENERAL KNOWLEDGE

1. Argus
2. Godric Gryffindor, Helga Hufflepuff, Rowena Ravenclaw & Salazar Slytherin
3. Never tickle a sleeping Dragon
4. Gameskeeper and Keeper of keys
5. Ordinary Wizarding Levels
6. Badger
7. Blue and Bronze
8. Seven
9. Armando Dippet
10. The bloody Baron
11. Minerva Mcgonagall, Dolores Umbridge & Severus Snape
12. 17 or 18
13. Bumblebee

14. Zonkos
15. Sweets
16. Diagon Alley
17. The Leaky Cauldron
18. The Daily Prophet
19. Books
20. Hogsmeade Station
21. Oak
22. It is the only All-Wizard village in Britain
23. Knockturn Alley
24. A vanishing step
25. The Kitchen
26. Staircases
27. Seven
28. 11am
29. Castle Ruins
30. Goblins
31. Professor Grubbly-Plank
32. Three
33. Seven
34. A barn owl
35. Ford Anglia
36. Radishes
37. love
38. Aberforth
39. Newt Scamander
40. Chudley Cannons
41. She's her daughteer
42. Avada Kedavra
43. Lily Potter
44. Red
45. A Dark Wizard catcher
46. A flesh memory
47. Causes everything that is touched to be multiplied
48. The Dark Mark
49. Allows you to revisit memories

50. In the Headmaster's office
51. Patronus
52. With a bow
53. Bathilda Bagshot
54. 1998
55. Six
56. By saying 'I solemnly swear that I am up to no good!'
57. Madam Pomfrey
58. Four
59. House elves
60. Their first year
61. A triangle a circle and a vertical line
62. Bertie Bott
63. Creates light at the end of the wand
64. Madame Maxime
65. Forces someone to tell the truth
66. Seven
67. Wingardium Leviosa
68. Three
69. Previous headmasters
70. Broken Parts of his wand
71. Evans

THE AUTHOR – J K ROWLING

1. 1965
2. Kathleen (the name of her Grandmother)
3. An old manual typewriter
4. 12
5. Casual Vacancy
6. Robert Galbraith
7. Harry Potter and the Cursed Child

8. Pottermore
9. On a Plane
10. That the whole cast was to be British
11. Her old Chemistry Teacher
12. 1995
13. Hufflepuff
14. Hermione

ON THE FILM SET

1. Eight
2. Harry & Ron
3. Four
4. Three
5. She was 37 and the oldest person to play one of the students
6. Head Lice
7. Warner Brothers
8. 160 pairs
9. Arachnophobia (fear of spiders)
10. Contact Lenses
11. The Chamber of Secrets
12. They were held with wires
13. A Tennis Ball
14. A dog called Max
15. Leavesdon
16. 2001
17. Warwick Davis
18. It becomes a shade lighter
19. 8ft 6"

TRUE OR FALSE

1. TRUE
2. FALSE
3. FALSE
4. TRUE
5. TRUE
6. FALSE
7. TRUE
8. FALSE
9. TRUE
10. TRUE
11. FALSE
12. FALSE
13. TRUE
14. FALSE
15. TRUE
16. FALSE
17. FALSE
18. TRUE
19. FALSE
20. FALSE
21. FALSE
22. TRUE
23. FALSE
24. TRUE
25. FALSE
26. FALSE
27. TRUE
28. FALSE
29. TRUE
30. FALSE
31. TRUE
32. FALSE
33. TRUE
34. TRUE
35. FALSE
36. TRUE
37. FALSE
38. TRUE
39. FALSE
40. TRUE
41. TRUE